WELCOME
LITERACY ACTIVITY BOOK

Senior Authors
J. David Cooper
John J. Pikulski

Authors
Kathryn H. Au
Margarita Calderón
Jacqueline C. Comas
Marjorie Y. Lipson
J. Sabrina Mims
Susan E. Page
Sheila W. Valencia
MaryEllen Vogt

Consultants
Dolores Malcolm
Tina Saldivar
Shane Templeton

INVITATIONS
TO LITERACY

Houghton Mifflin Company • Boston

Atlanta • Dallas • Geneva, Illinois • Palo Alto • Princeton

CONTENTS

MAGIC PICTURES

Consonant Sounds and Letters

Bb
bird

Cc
cat

Dd
dinosaur

Ff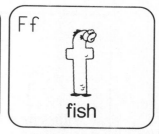
fish

Gg
ghost

Hh
horse

Jj
jack-in-the-box

Kk
king

Ll
lion

Mm
monster

Nn
nurse

Pp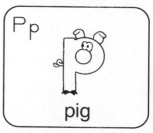
pig

Qq
queen

Rr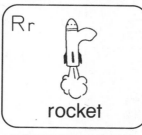
rocket

Ss
seal

Tt
tiger

Vv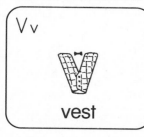
vest

Ww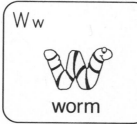
worm

Yy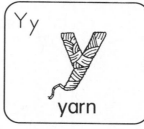
yarn

Zz
zebra

MAGIC PICTURES

Vowel Sounds and Letters

A a

alligator

acorn

E e

elephant

eel

I i
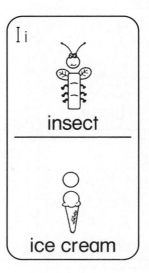
insect

ice cream

O o

ostrich

ocean

U u

umbrella

unicorn

Name _____

Show and Tell

 Add details to finish the picture.

 Then write about your picture.

_____

- -

_____

- -

_____

It's Time for School

✏️ Think of each beginning sound. Write **b** or **t**.

🖍️ Color red the pictures whose names begin like 🐦.

Color yellow the pictures whose names begin like 🐯.

Name _____

Find It!

✏️ **Circle the word that names each picture.**

LOST AND FOUND

ball	bag
tack	top
boat	book
tape	toy

🖍️ **Draw something whose name begins like  or that
might be in the Lost and Found.**

✏️ **Write the word that names
your picture.** _____

 Off We Go—See What We Know! **5**

Name

Busy Day

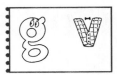

✏️▷ **Think of each beginning sound. Write g or v.**

✏️▷ **Draw a line from each letter you wrote to the**

correct lunch box.

Name _____

What's for Lunch?

✏️ **Draw a line from the picture to the word it goes with.**

1

van

bat

3

take

gate

2

bird

girl

4

vine

time

🖍️ **Draw something whose name begins like** **or** 🧥 **that might be on a lunch box.**

✏️ **Write the word that names your picture.**

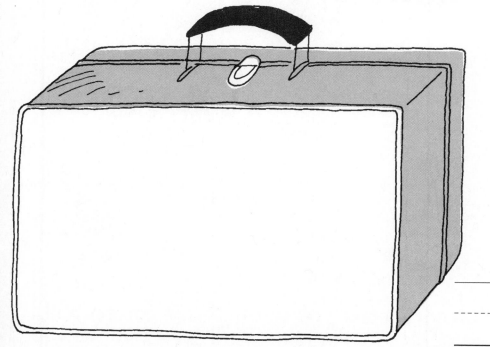

_____

- - - - - - - - - - - - - - - - - - -

_____

Off We Go—See What We Know!   **7**

Name

Play Time

✏️ Think of each beginning sound.

Write **k**, **m**, or **z**.

✏️ Draw a line from each letter you wrote to the correct ball.

Name

Keep Moving!

✏️ **Circle the word that names each picture.**

zip
get

tell
march

bake
kick

mix
tip

🖍️ **Draw something you can do in school whose name**

begins like 👑 , 🐵 , **or** 🦓 .

✏️ **Write the word that names the action.**

Off We Go—See What We Know!

9

Name

Run and Jump!

 Color the picture that goes with each sentence.

1 All the  run.

2 The 🐱🐱 jump up.

3 I jump all the time.

Name _____

What Are They Doing?

✂ **Cut out the words.**

**Paste them under the pictures to
tell what the people are doing.**

 **On the back of this paper, draw you and a friend
doing one of these things.** ➡

jumping	drawing
counting	kicking

Off We Go—See What We Know!

15

Name _____

My Alphabet Page

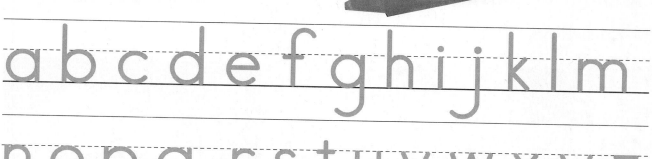

✏️➤ Trace the letters.

abcdefghijklm

nopqrstuvwxyz

🖍️➤ Draw a picture of a game you play at school.

✏️➤ Write the letter the name of your game begins with.

Write the name of your game.

_____

_____

 Off We Go—See What We Know! **13**

Name

Then What?

 Start at each barn door. Draw a line to show
what will happen next.

 Draw and write about what will happen next.

Name _____

At the Farm

✏️ **Think of each beginning sound. Write c or d.**

✏️ **Draw a line from each letter you wrote to the correct window.**

 Off We Go—See What We Know! **15**

Behind the Barn

✏️ Draw a line to connect each speech

to the animal that is saying it.

I run up
the **dock**.

I make the
cook run.

I take the
corn.

✏️ **Now label the pictures.**

_____

- - - - - - - - -

_____

Name _____

Vegetables for Sale!

✏️ **Think of each beginning sound.**

Write j, p, or r.

🖍️ **Color blue the pictures whose names begin like** 📦 .

Color orange the pictures whose names begin like 🐷 .

Color brown the pictures whose names begin like 🚀 .

 Off We Go—See What We Know! **17**

Name

Pig's Farm

✏️ Circle the word that names each picture.

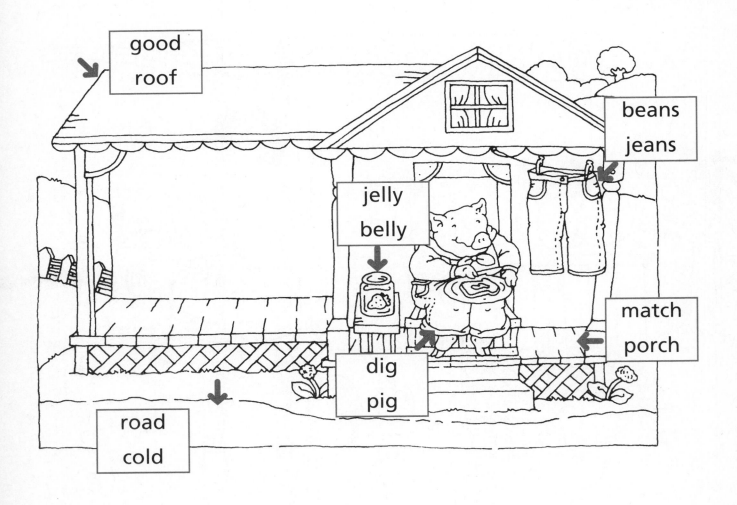

good
roof

beans
jeans

jelly
belly

dig
pig

match
porch

road
cold

🖍️ **Think of something whose name begins like** **,** 🐷 **,**

or 🚀 **. Draw your idea on Pig's farm.**

✏️ **Write the word that names your picture.**

_____

- -

_____

Name _____

What's in the Barn?

✎ **Think of each beginning sound. Write n or y.**

🖍 **Color green the pictures whose names begin like** 👩‍⚕️.

Color yellow the pictures whose names begin like 🧶 .

 Off We Go—See What We Know! **19**

Name

Farmhouse Food

Read the story.

Cat bakes all **night**.

Cat makes **noodles**.

Cat takes a **nap**.
Dog rakes the **yard**.

Draw a picture of something whose name begins like 👩‍⚕️

or 🧶 for the animals to eat.

Write the word that names your picture.

Name _____

One Brown Bat

went	one
cats	fast

✏️ Use the words to finish each sentence.
The pictures will help you.

_____

1 One rooster _____ up.

2 Two _____ jump.

3 Three dogs run _____ .

4 And _____ bat zips past.

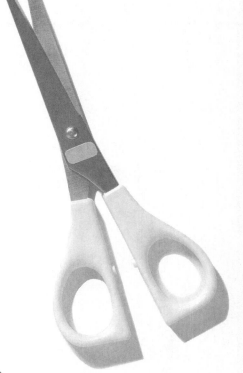

✂️ Cut out and paste the pictures in the barn
on the back of this page.   ➡️

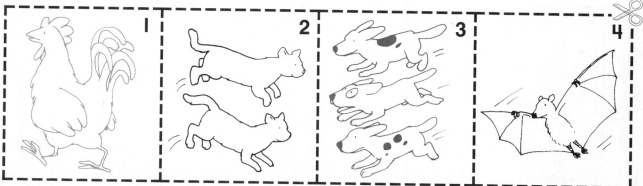

 Off We Go—See What We Know!   21

Name

Color It!

▶ Use the color key to finish the picture.

| **1** = red | **2** = blue | **3** = black |
| **4** = yellow | **5** = brown | **6** = pink |

▶ Write about what you see.

_____

- -

_____

- -

_____

Name

How Many Animals?

 Color the animals in each picture.

Count them. Write the number and word.

one	six
two	seven
three	eight
four	nine
five	ten

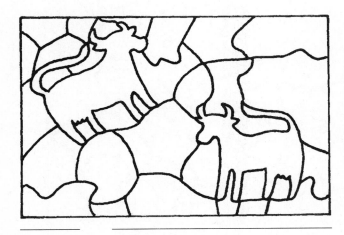

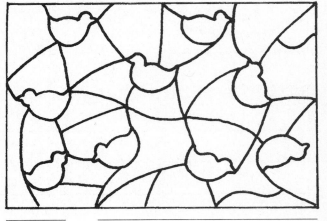

Name

Make Them the Same

✂ **Cut out the shapes at the bottom of the page.**

Paste them on to make the pictures match.

Off We Go—See What We Know! **25**

Name

Feel the Sand

✏️ **Think of each beginning sound. Write f or s.**

KEEP OFF THE
DUNES

✏️ **Draw a line from each letter you wrote to the**

correct umbrella.

Name _____

Tasty Treats

✏️ Circle the word that names each picture.

✏️ Then draw something for the table that begins

like 🐟 or 🦭 .

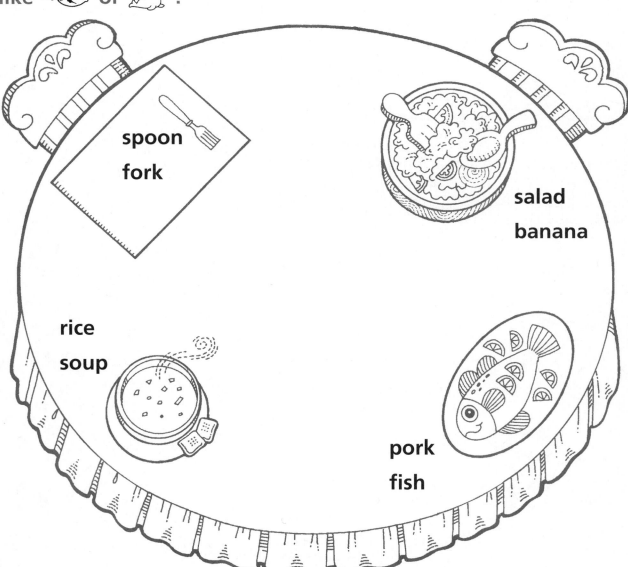

spoon

fork

salad

banana

rice

soup

pork

fish

✏️ Write a word that names your picture.

_____

- -

_____

Name

What Do You See?

✏️ **Think of each beginning sound. Write h or qu.**

🖍️ **Color brown the pictures whose names begin like** **.**

Color yellow the pictures whose names begin like 👑 **.**

Name

Help the Queen!

Read the story.

The **queen has** a rip!

The **queen's heel** tips!

Help! Quick!

 Choose one of the pictures.

Draw how it can help the queen. Label your picture.

Use Your Senses

✏️ **Think of each beginning sound. Write l or w.**

✏️ **Draw a line from each letter you wrote to the correct jar.**

 Off We Go—See What We Know! **31**

Name

See Three Dogs

Read the story.

1. **Look!** Three dogs **wear** hats!

2. Three dogs **leap**!

3. Three dogs **wave**!

4. The dogs make me **laugh**!

✏️ **Write something the dogs could do that begins like  or .**

_____

- -

_____

Name _____

Do You See?

Read the story.

 **Draw what the baby will do next.**

Write about your picture.

_____

- - - - - - - - - - - - - - - - - -

_____

- - - - - - - - - - - - - - - - - -

_____

Body Language

 Draw eyes, a nose, and a mouth on the person. Then draw ears and hands.

eyes	nose
ears	hands
mouth	

Write the name of each part.

Draw a line from each label to the picture.

All About Me

Draw a picture of yourself.

Finish the sentences about you.

My name is _____.

I like to play _____.

I like to eat _____.

✂ **Cut out the picture. Hang it where others can see it.**

Off We Go—See What We Know! **35**

Name

Make a 1-2-3-4

✂ Cut out these things and paste them in your Number Book.

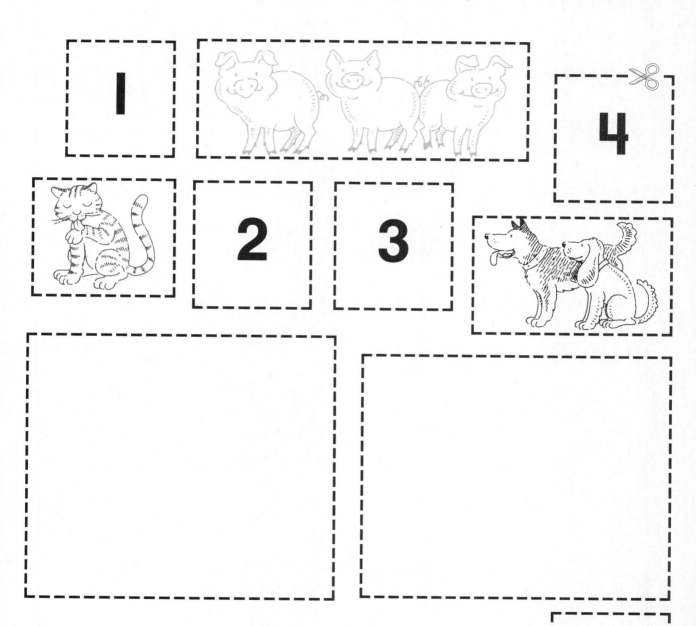

☐ Did I put a number on each page of my book?

☐ Did I put an animal name on each page?

☐ Did I make the right number of animals?

What Belongs Here?

✏️ Circle the two things in each box that go together.

Write the name of the group they belong in.

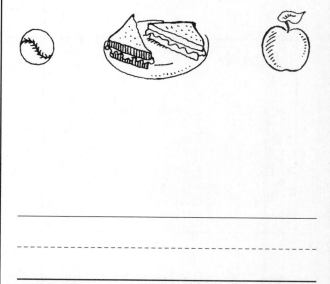

🖍 **Draw something else that belongs in each group.**

 Growing and Changing 39

Calendar Pictures

| f | s | t |

✏️➤ **Think of each ending sound. Write f, s, or t.**

January

_____
- - - - - - -
_____

April

_____
- - - - - - -
_____

February

_____
- - - - - - -
_____

May

_____
- - - - - - -
_____

March

_____
- - - - - - -
_____

June

_____
- - - - - - -
_____

✏️➤ **Draw a box around each picture whose name ends**

like 🚌 . **Circle each picture whose name ends like** 🚤 .

Name _____

What's in the Box?

| f | s | t |

✏️ Write **f**, **s**, or **t** to spell each word.

coa _____

rock _____

lea _____

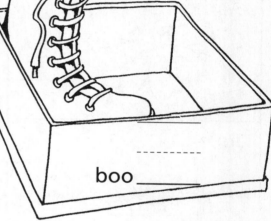

boo _____

Read the sentence.

🖍 Draw a picture to go with it.

Put the **rocks** with the **leaf**.

Name _____

Spring, Summer, Fall

✏️ **Think of each ending sound. Write l or r.**

April 	**July**
May	**August**
June	**September**

🖍️ Color blue the pictures whose names end like ⊛ .

Color orange the pictures whose names end like 🫙 .

Then read the names of the months with your teacher.

Underline the months that end with the sound l or r.

Name _____

Boxes to Fill

 Draw a line from the picture to the word it goes with.

  tool

bear

wheel

Write a word that ends like ⊛ or 🫙 to finish the last sentence.

I have one **car**.

_____

You have one _____ .

Draw a picture to go with your sentence.

 **Growing and Changing** 43

Name

One, Two, Three

✏️ **Choose a word from the box to finish each**
sentence. Draw and write an ending for the story.

for	it
will	is

1

It _____ not for the dog.

2

Is _____ for the cat?

3

It is _____ you.

But _____ three fit?

4

_____

_____

_____

_____

Name _____

Fun All Year

Can you name the months of the year?

January	February	March	April
May	June	July	August
September	October	November	December

✏️ **Write an ending to each sentence.**

✂️ **Then cut and paste a picture to go with your sentence.**

In April and May, I smell

_____

- -

_____

In July and August, I play with a

_____

- -

_____

In October and November, I grow a

_____

- -

_____

Name

My Special Things

✏️ **Write a list of things you like to save and keep.**

① _____

② _____

③ _____

④ _____

 🖍️ **Draw a picture to show where you keep your things.**

Name _____

What Would They Say?

✏️ Write **Me too!** or **Not me!** in the speech balloons to show what the animals and children would say.

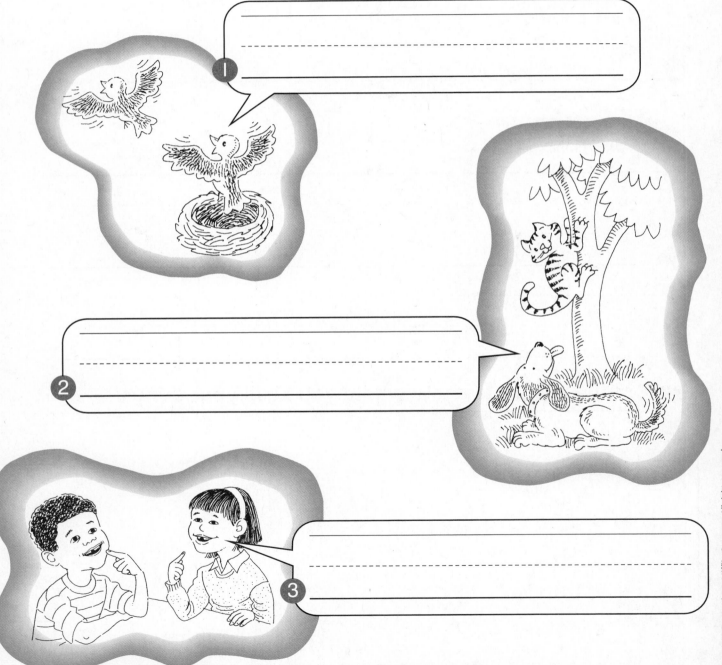

The Chick and the Duckling
PHONICS AND SPELLING
Final Consonants: *k, m*

Name

Busy Birds

k   m

✏️ See what the birds have. Think of each

ending sound. Write **k** or **m**.

✏️ Circle each picture that ends like 🍴 .

Mark an **X** on each picture that ends like 🥁 .

The Chick and the Duckling
PHONICS AND SPELLING
Final Consonants: *k, m*

Name

Go, Duck!

| k | m |

Draw a line to connect each sentence to the picture it goes with.

1 I **walk**.   **2** I **look**.   **3** I **swim**.   **4** I **dream**.

Write a word that ends like  or to finish the sentence.

I will _____ with the .

Draw a picture to go with your sentence.

The Chick and the Duckling
PHONICS AND SPELLING
Final Consonants: *b, g*

Name

Help the Duckling

| b | g |

✏️ **Think of each ending sound. Write b or g.**

✏️ **Help the Duckling find his way to the stream.**

Follow the path with pictures whose names end like .

The Chick and the Duckling
PHONICS AND SPELLING
Final Consonants: *b, g*

Name _____

Dig This!

> Read each sentence and draw a speech balloon around it. Then draw a line to connect each speech balloon to the picture it goes with.

1 I **sob**.

2 We **jog**.

3 I **dig**.

> Write a word that ends like 🛏 or 🐕 to finish the sentence.

_____

Will you _____ with me,   ?

> Draw a picture to go with your sentence.

Name

Not Me!

 Read the story. Cut out and paste each picture in the box where it belongs.

1	**2**
Duck came to see Dog. "I am Duck," he said. Dog said, "I am Dog."	Cat came to see Duck and Dog. "I am Cat," he said.
3	**4**
"I will jump," said Duck. "Me too," said Dog.	"Not me," said Cat. "I will not jump!"

Growing and Changing **53**

✏️ **What do you think Cat will do now? Write about Cat.**

_____

- -

_____

_____

- -

_____

_____

- -

_____

_____

- -

_____

Name _____

Who Are You?

| I am = I'm | I will = I'll |

✏️ Write the sentences again, using **I'm** and **I'll**.
Then color the pictures.

I am a dog. I will run.

_____
- - - - - - - - - - - - - - - - - - - -
_____

I am a cat. I will jump.

_____
- - - - - - - - - - - - - - - - - - - -
_____

I am a chick. I will run and jump too!

_____
- - - - - - - - - - - - - - - - - - - -
_____
- - - - - - - - - - - - - - - - - - - -
_____

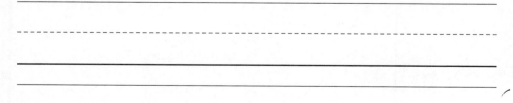

Name

Lost!

 Help the baby animals find their mothers. Draw a line from each animal to its mother. Then write the animal names next to their pictures.

piglet

calf

duck

duckling

pig

cow

Name

How to Grow a Pumpkin

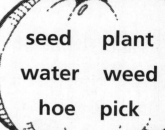

How would you grow a pumpkin? Draw pictures to show what you would do first, next, and last.

Next to each picture, write about what you would do. You might use the words in the pumpkin.

seed   plant
water   weed
hoe   pick

First,

Next,

Last,

Name

In the Garden

d	n

✏️ **Think of each ending sound. Write d or n.**

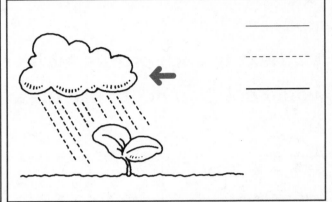

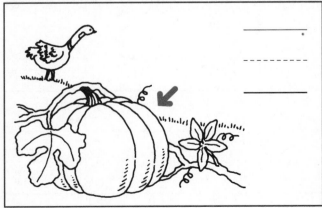

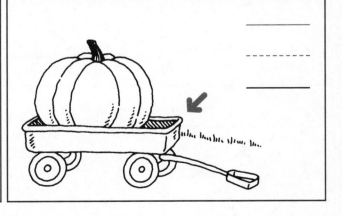

🖍️ **Color green the pictures that end like** **.**

Color brown the pictures that end like **.**

What's Outside?

d	n

✏️ **Write each word next to the picture it goes with.**

moon	garden	wood	road

🖍️ **Draw a picture of something you might see outside.**

 Growing and Changing 59

Name

In the Yard

| p | x |

✏️ **Think of each ending sound. Write p or x.**

✏️ Circle each picture that ends like 🖼️.

Mark an **X** on each picture that ends like 6.

Name

Pumpkin Time

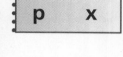

✏️ **Draw a line to connect each picture to the sentence it goes with.**

  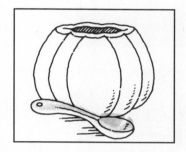

The **pup** jumps up.   The **box** is for you.   It is time to **scoop**.

✏️ **Write two words that end like  or 6️⃣ to finish the sentence.**

_____

- -

I have a _____ for the dog and a

_____

- -

_____ for the pup.

🖍️ **Draw a picture to go with your sentence.**

Name

Out, Dog!

Use the words to write a sentence about each picture. Then color the pictures.

| six | We | in | plants. | put |

_____

| came | dog | in. | a | Then |

| went | The | out | fast. | dog |

One, Two, Three, Jump!

✏️ Read the story and circle the word endings.
Then cut and paste a picture to go with each sentence.

1 I am planting.

2 The cat is jumping.

3 The baby jumps too.

4 I planted all my plants.

5 Then I jumped too!

 Growing and Changing 63

✏️ Write your own sentence using a word with an ending. Here are some words you can use.

runs	needed	fixing	seeds	mixed	wins

Name ______________________________

Garden Work

Color the picture.

Finish the sentences. Use the words from the box.

1. The man ______________ a hole.
2. The girl ______________ the seed.
3. The boy ______________ an apple.

picks
digs
plants

Name _____

Making Little-Big Cards

 Plan what you will draw on your cards.

Little	Big

Did you?

☐ Did you draw two animals or plants in each set?

☐ Did you make one little and one big?

Name of Book

Name of Book

Name of Book

Name of Book

Name of Book

Name of Book

Name of Book

MY FAVORITE STORIES

Name of Book

Name of Book

Name of Book

Name of Book

Name of Book

Name of Book

Name of Book

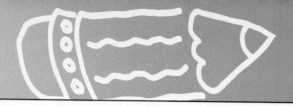

✏️ **Trace and write the letters.**

Aa Aa

Bb Bb

Cc Cc

Dd Dd

Ee Ee

Ff Ff

Gg Gg

WRITING THE ALPHABET

✏️ **Trace and write the letters.**

Hh Hh

Ii Ii

Jj Jj

Kk Kk

Ll Ll

Mm Mm

✏️ **Trace and write the letters.**

Nn Nn

Oo Oo

Pp Pp

Qq Qq

Rr Rr

Ss Ss

Tt Tt

WRITING THE ALPHABET

✏️ **Trace and write the letters.**

Uu Uu

Vv Vv

Ww Ww

Xx Xx

Yy Yy

Zz Zz

✏️ **Trace and write the letters.**

Aa Aa

Bb Bb

Cc Cc

Dd Dd

Ee Ee

Ff Ff

Gg Gg

✏️ **Trace and write the letters.**

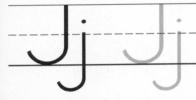

 **Trace and write the letters.**

Nn Nn

Oo Oo

Pp Pp

Qq Qq

Rr Rr

Ss Ss

Tt Tt

✏️ **Trace and write the letters.**

A	A	A	B	B	C	C	D	D
E	E	E	F	F	G	G	H	H
I	I	J	J	K	K	L	L	M
M	N	N	O	O	P	P	Q	Q
R	R	S	S	T	T	U	U	V
V	W	W	X	X	Y	Y	Z	Z

fold

fold

fold

d	d	c	c	b	b	a	a	a
h	h	g	g	f	f	e	e	e
m	l	l	k	k	j	j	i	i
q	q	p	p	o	o	n	n	m
v	u	u	t	t	s	s	r	r
z	z	y	y	x	x	w	w	v

fold

fold

fold

WHEN THIS BOX IS FULL	MY FIVE SENSES	ONE RED ROOSTER	ANNIE, BEA, AND CHI CHI DOLORES
High-Frequency Words	High-Frequency Words	High-Frequency Words	High-Frequency Words
but	a	and	all
?	?	?	?
for	baby	cat	I
?	?	?	?
is	have	dog	jump
?	?	?	?
it	my	fast	run
?	?	?	?
not	our	one	the
?	?	?	?
will	see	three	time
?	?	?	?
you	we	two	up
?	?	?	?
	with	went	
?	?	?	?
?	?	?	?
?	?	?	?

ANNIE, BEA, AND CHI CHI DOLORES	ONE RED ROOSTER	MY FIVE SENSES	WHEN THIS BOX IS FULL
?	?	?	?
?	?	?	?
?	?	?	?
?	?	?	?
?	?	?	?
?	?	?	?
?	?	?	?
?	?	?	?
?	?	?	?
?	?	?	?

| NUMBER WORDS | COLOR WORDS | PUMPKIN PUMPKIN | THE CHICK AND THE DUCKLING |
		High-Frequency Words	High-Frequency Words
one	red	in	am
?	?	?	?
two	yellow	out	came
?	?	?	?
three	blue	plant	he
?	?	?	?
four	green	put	me
?	?	?	?
five	pink	six	said
?	?	?	?
six	purple	then	too
?	?	?	?
seven	white		
?	?	?	?
eight	brown		
?	?	?	?
nine	black		
?	?	?	?
ten	orange		
?	?	?	?

THE CHICK AND THE DUCKLING	PUMPKIN PUMPKIN	COLOR WORDS	NUMBER WORDS
?	?	?	?
?	?	?	?
?	?	?	?
?	?	?	?
?	?	?	?
?	?	?	?
?	?	?	?
?	?	?	?
?	?	?	?
?	?	?	?

with	one	all
but	three	I
for	two	jump
is	went	run
it	a	the
not	baby	time
will	have	up
you	my	and
am	our	cat
came	see	dog
he	we	fast

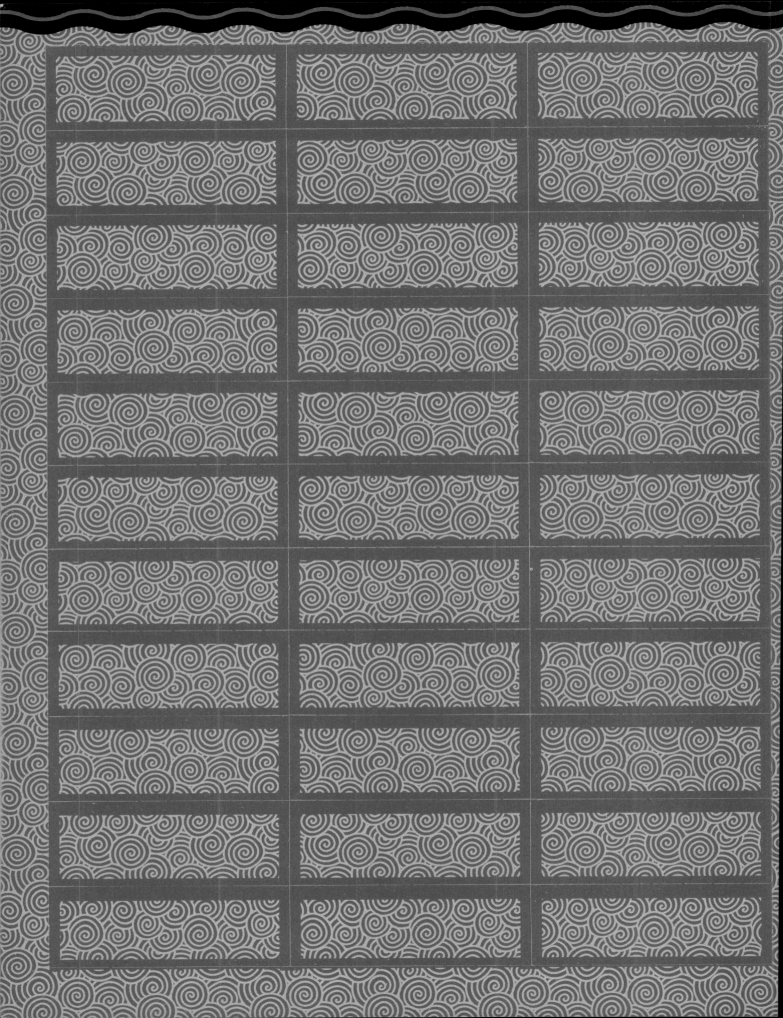